Tree-
House
Comix
Proudly
Presents

DOG MAN
TWENTY THOUSAND FLEAS Under The Sea

WRITTEN AND ILLUSTRATED BY **DAV PILKEY**

AS GEORGE BEARD AND HAROLD HUTCHINS

WITH COLOR BY JOSE GARIBALDI & WES DZIOBA

graphix

AN IMPRINT OF

■SCHOLASTIC

Library of Congress Control Number 2022944016

978-1-338-80191-0 (POB)
978-1-338-80192-7 (Library)

10 9 8 7 6 5 4 3 2 1   23 24 25 26 27

Printed in the U.S.A.   61
First edition, March 2023

Editorial team: Ken Geist and Jonah Newman
Book design by Dav Pilkey and Phil Falco
Color by Jose Garibaldi and Wes Dzioba
Color flatting by Aaron Polk and Corey Barba
Creative Director: Phil Falco
Publisher: David Saylor

CHAPTERS

Meet the Cast...4

Chapter 1. Dog Man Jumps the Shark 7

Chapter 2. Mini Jail 33

Chapter 3. Helping Papa 47

Chapter 4. Bad Mister Stinkles...............................61

Chapter 5. A Buncha Stuff That
            Happened Next....................................73

Chapter 6. Friendly Friends Are GO! 99

Chapter 7. Cat Cell Culture...................................113

Chapter 8. BREAKING NEWS: TWENTY
            THOUSAND FLEAS UNDER THE
            THE SEA..127

Chapter 9. Follow That Sub 137

Chapter 10. Pie Fight..145

Chapter 11. Piggy Makes His Move.......................159

Chapter 12. Zoom In 173

Chapter 13. This Mite Be a Problem.....................185

Chapter 14. And Then There Were Two..................203

Chapter 15. Exactly One Hundred and
            Nine Seconds Earlier 215

Chapter 16. In Search of the Depth 225

How to Draw...236

Notes & Fun Facts...240

MEET THE CAST

DOG MAN: He's part dog, part man, and ALL HERO! Sometimes he dresses up as a superhero named "The Bark Knight," although he has no superpowers.

PETEY: He used to be an irritable, impatient bad guy. But when his son arrived, Petey became determined to change his ways. Now he's an irritable, impatient Good Guy.

LI'L PETEY: Petey's pure-hearted son. He loves making comics and telling jokes. Sometimes he even saves the world as a superhero named "Cat Kid."

MOLLY: She may *look* like a tadpole, but she identifies as a baby frog. Her superpower is *psychokinesis*, which means that she can move things with her mind.

SARAH HATOFF & ZUZU: Sarah is an investigative journalist from Australia who adores her pet poodle, Zuzu. Sarah always carries a purse, too, except when Harold forgets to draw it.

4

CHIEF: He's Dog Man's brave boss and loyal best friend. Chief also has a HUGE CRUSH on Nurse Lady. Don't tell anybody!!!

NURSE LADY (a.k.a. Genie S. Lady, RN, BSN): She's a smart and brave health-care professional, and her quick thinking saved Dog Man's life. She also has a MAJOR CRUSH on Chief. Shhh!!!!

80-HD: A robot designed by Petey and rebuilt by Li'l Petey. Although his exoskeleton houses a limitless supply of helpful gadgets, his greatest superpower is CREATIVITY.

PIGGY: He's the ruthless leader of the FLEAS, which is an acronym for "Fuzzy Little Evil Animal Squad." Recently, Piggy got shrunk by a shrink ray, and was locked up in Mini Jail for "Crimes and stuff."

CRUNKY & BUB: Piggy's sidekicks and members of the FLEAS. Crunky (the gorilla) and Bub (the crocodile) also got shrunk and locked up in Mini Jail, but unlike Piggy, they're both pretty good guys.

DARYL: He's a friendly moth who founded a superhero club called "The Friendly Friends." Daryl is a loyal friend to Piggy, even though Piggy is mean and rude in return.

For my brother,
Steve Aragaki

CHAPTER 1

DOG MAN JUMPS THE SHARK

We're almost there!

Thanks for coming with me on my date, DoG Man!!!

I'm a little **nervous!**

Is my breath okay?

sniff
sniff

Oh, boy! This is Gonna be...

...GREAT! She's already HERE!!!

SHARK SHACK

What do I **<u>DO</u>**, Dog Man?

What do I **SAY?**

What if she doesn't **LiKE** me anymore???

Push Push Push

He's not a <u>Do</u>G.

He's **DOG MAN!**

Well he looks like a DoG to **ME!!!**

And we don't **ALLOW DOGS!**

Oh, Yeah? Well I don't see a **SiGN!!!**

...and tie him to this **TRASH CAN** where he belongs!

Now he can't cause **ANY TROUBLE!!!**

HAW HAW HAW!!!

HAW HAW HAW HAW HAW HAW

ZIP

STEP 1.
First, place your left hand inside the dotted lines marked "Left hand here." Hold the book open FLAT!

STEP 2:
Grasp the right-hand page with your thumb and index finger (inside the dotted lines marked "Right Thumb Here").

STEP 3:
Now quickly flip the right-hand page back and forth until the picture appears to be Animated.

(for extra fun, try adding your own sound-effects!)

O.RAMA

..FOR A Bold, New World

LET THE FIGHT BEGIN

Left hand here.

Date Fight

Right
Thumb
here.

Date Fight

And so...

Are You okay, DoG Man?

Welp, I Guess We better Go!!!

Okay! But first...

CHAPTER 2

Mini JaiL

By George Beard and Harold Hutchins

Wanna try one?

NO, I DON'T WANNA TRY A CUPCAKE!!!

I'M NOT EVEN HUNGRY ANYMORE!

YOU GUYS MADE ME LOSE MY APPETITE!!

HOW COULD YOU BE SO SELFISH???

Soon... Hiya, Piggy!

Well? Did you bring it???

Aren't you even going to say hello?

Hello, DARYL! Did you bring the CANNERY GROW?

No!

It's your **COSTUME!!!**

COSTUME?? What For?

For our **CLUB,** Piggy!!!

Don't you remember the **Friendly Friends?**

I Just recruited **TWO** **NEW Members!**

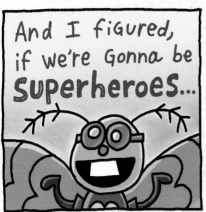

And I figured, if we're Gonna be **Superheroes**...

...We're Gonna need **COSTUMES!**

These are the **MOST RIDICULOUS COSTUMES** I've **EVER Seen!**

They Look Like BABY CLOTHES!!!

WHO Would be DUMB Enough To WEAR SomeThing Like THIS?

46

CHAPTER 3
HELPING PAPA

FLiP FLoP FLiP FLoP FLiP FLoP FLiP

ALRIGHT, WE'VE GOT A **LOT** OF **WORK** to do...

...So I don't want you two **PLAYING!!!**

Why?

Because we've Got to **Rebuild** our **LAB!!!**

Why?

Because **I** need a Place to **Live**!!!

Why?

Because I can't keep living at DoG Man's house!

Why?

FLiP FLOP   FLIP FLOP   FLiP FLOP

BECAUSE YOU GUYS ARE SOOOO IRRiTATiNG!!!

Why?

Because You're **NOISY**...

...You're **MESSY**...

... And You think **everything** is **SOOOO HiLARiOUS!!!**

Why?

Because You—

CUT THAT OUT!

Why?

ARE YOU JUST GOING TO BE A **WISE GUY** ALL DAY???

Yeah, Probably.

WELL, THAT'S JUST **GREAT!**

You **PROMISED** to be **GOOD** todAY!!!

You **BEGGED** to come with me!!!

You **SWORE** to be helpful!!!

But we haven't even **STARTED**...

... And You're **ALREADY** being A **BIG PAIN!!!**

I'm sorry, Papa.

This is **NOT PLAY-Time!**

Do You hear me?

You Are **NOT** here to **PLAY!**

Chapter 4
BAD MISTER STINKLES

Left hand here.

...YOU Drop that MAXimum Security CORRectionaL FACiLity _Right NOW_!!!

Right Thumb here.

...YOU Drop that MAXimum Security CORRectionaL FaciLity *Right* *Now*!!!

Meanwhile...

Hey, Look! It's a **SWING!**

Let's swing on it!!!

Gee whiz. Do you think it's **SAFE?**

Of course it's safe...

CHOMP -O- RAMA

Left hand here.

...what could **POSSIBLY**
Go **WRONG?**

Right
Thumb
here.

...what could **POSSibLY**
Go **WRONG?**

78

I'm — I'm sorry, Nurse Lady.

I'm sorry, too.

Sorry we didn't try that **SOONER!**

LET'S DO IT AGAIN!!!

C'mon, fellas!

Meanwhile...

DONNA'S CONSTRUCTION

OK, Mr. TheCat...

I'll help you rebuild your lab.

Let's Get started!

CTION

HEY, look! There he is!!!

Flip Flop Flip Flop Flip

Look, I apprecia[te]

Your breath smells like coffee.

I APPRECIATE YOUR GIFT...

...But I DON'T have Time to READ it Right NOW!!!

That's okay, Wally!

I'LL read it FOR You!!!

SLAP!

One time Wally was in a **BAD MOOD.**

"as usual!"

First, he slipped on a banana peel...

zip

Then he fell down the stairs...

...then a bee stung his butt.

~~You~~ I'm MAD!

So I'm gonna build my own world...

84

Well? Did ya like it, Wally?

NO!!!

It doesn't even make **sense!**

And why was the last part **BLANK?**

Oh. We couldn't think of an ending.

Or a middle.

89

We're Sorry, Wally.

AND MY NAME's **NOT WALLY!**

It's **PETEY!**

PETEY!!!

PETEY THE CAT!

Wait— **YOU'RE** _Petey_ the Cat?

Yeah.

Aren't you the guy who stole all of those **toilets**...

...And made everybody wet their pants???

Um... that—

—That was a **LONG TIME AGO.**

I've already been **Punished** for that!

I paid my **Debt to Society!**

AND the Governor **PARDONED** me!

Ever since then, I've lived my—

HEY! Where are You Going ???

AWAY FROM You!

But You **SAID** You'd help me **Rebuild** my **LAb!**

Beats me, Mike!

Let's find out!!!

Hey, Look! It's Crunky And Bub!!!

And they're CRYING!

Should we help them?

Okay!

And So...

WAAAA AAA

We're helping YOU CRY!

Thanks, Ducky!

If only you could help us **FLY!!!**

We can do **that!**

FWOOSH

FWOOSH!

CHAPTER 6
FRIENDLY FRIENDS ARE GO!

Meanwhile...

Aaah— Freedom at Last!!!

But I miss Crunky and Bub!

Would You Forget About those Guys?

They're Nothing But TROUBLE!!!

ALL they do is EAT, LAUGH...

...And make up RiDiCULOUS SONGS!!!

NOTE: THIS SONG can be sung to the tune of "Jingle Bells."

Friendly Friends, Friendly Friends...

...Armed with Friendly Hugs...

...OH, What Fun it is to Ride...

...on the BACKS of Friendly Bugs!

DASHING Through The Sky...

...on a beetle, moth, and FLY...

...O'er the hills So high...

...LAUGHING TILL we CRY!

HA! HA! WAA!

SOARING THROUGH the AIR...

...SWOOPING here and there...

...What Fun it is to Share and CARE...

Left
hand here

GRR-FACE A GO-GO!

Right Thumb here.

GRR-FACE A GO-GO!

What **IS** this Place?

It's the **FRIENDLY FRIENDS ACTION HEADQUARTERS!**

We can use this technology...

... to spread JOY and Sunshine **ALL** over the **WORLD!**

Yeeeah...

... that's **EXACTLY** What **I** was thinking!

CHAPTER 7

CAT CELL CULTURE

...and my hand hurts...

... and it's too sunny...

No excuses construction

...and my truck won't start...

How come nobody will help us?

Because I went to Jail...

...and I- **HEY!**

I told You this storY in the **LAST BOOK!**

Oh. Oh.

We Probably weren't listening.

Yeah! Tell us **AGAiN!**

What's the Point???

I **TRY** to **DO GOOD!**

I **TRY** and I **TRY**...

... but nobody cares.

I'll **ALWAYS** be the bad guy.

Meanwhile...

RUFF RUFF RUFF R

That sounds like DoG Man!!!

RUFF RUFF

COME on, ZUZU!

RUFF RUFF Ru

What's **WRONG**, DoG Man?

Something's up at The Beach?

UNDER their roof?

Under the...

...under the "**C**"?

Umm... is it **ITChY?**

Is it fleas?

They're at The Beach under the "C."

At the **beach?** Under the **Sea?**

Yeah. It's where they make those Supa-sized Subs!

They're MAKING SUBS?

OH, NO!!!

click

I better tell the Boss!!!

Two minutes Later...

SUPA-SizeD SUBMARines?

Yeah! And there are **MORE** than **EVER!!!**

THAT'S A SWELL SCOOP!!!

BuT WE GoTTA Punch it UP!!!

Give it some **MOXie!!!**

CHAPTER 8

BREAKING NEWS

TWENTY THOUSAND FLEAS

UNDER THE THE SEA

DEATH SUB FOR PIGGY

Photo Collage Illustration

INVASION ALERT!!!

ANONYMOUS AUTHORITIES FEAR DOOMSDAY

Does Piggy plan to **DESTROY** our way of of life with his **BLOODTHRISTY, KILLER SUBS**?

Click here to learn how **YOU** can **SAVE YOUR** way of life for only $19.99 per month. **Act NOW!!!**

JOIN THE "FLEAS ARE REALLY TERRIBLE SOCIETY" TODAY!

Click here to resell "FLEAS ARE REALLY TERRIBLE SOCIETY" (FARTS) Merchandise.

Click here to save on "FLEAS ARE REALLY TERRIBLE SOCIETY" Tattoo Removals.

DOCTORS RECOMMMEND NEW "SUPA FLEA SPRAY"

Click here to save 10% on SUPA FLEA SPRAY side-effects remedies.

Click here to save 5% on remedy for side-effects of SUPA FLEA SPRAY side-effect remedies.

Meanwhile...

This place is **AMAZING!!!**

Thanks, PIGGY! MY Uncle Larry built it all.

He's a **Genius!**

Aw, shucks!!!

And what is **THAT?**

Oh, that? It's a **FLYING Sub!**

It's **Beautiful!**

And the **Best PART** is...

I've Got the **WHOLE PLACE** to **MYSELF!!!**

Don't worry, Piggy...

...Watch **this!!!**

SIZE -O- TRON

SUPA DOOPA BIG
SUPA BIG
BIG
NORMAL
SMALL
SUPA SMALL
SUPA DOOPA SMALL

Our built-in **Size-O-Tron** can make this sub **SHRiNK!!!**

KA-KLUNK

SIZE -O- TRON

SUPA DOOPA BIG
SUPA BIG
BIG
NORMAL
SMALL
SUPA SMALL
SUPA DOOPA SMALL
SUPA DOOPA PooP

SUB WILL SHRINK IN FIVE SECONDS...

...FOUR...

...THREE...

... TWO ...

... ONE ...

SHRINKING
NOW

133

And so...

Nice Job, Uncle Larry!!!

Aw, shucks!

Now can You make us Grow **SUPA BiG?**

I Sure can!!!

Size -O- TRON

SUPA DOOPA BiG
SUPA BiG
BiG
NORMAL
SMALL

KA KLUNK

SUB WILL GROW IN FIVE SECONDS...

But then...

Hey!!!

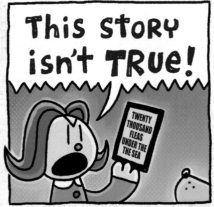

This STORY isn't TRUE!

TWENTY THOUSAND FLEAS UNDER THE THE SEA

I NEVER SAID TWENTY THOUSAND!

I NEVER SAID there were SUBMARINES!

SUBMARINE ALERT

SHA SHA SHA

I Never...

SHA SHA SHA

...never...

SHA SHA SHA

Umm...

...Never mind.

CHAPTER 9

FOLLOW THAT SUB

We interrupt this story with a **TERRIFYING** Report!

The MEDIA

All across the beach...

...Protesters have Gathered to oppose **TWENTY THOUSAND FLEAS...**

Fight the FLEAS

FLEAS

Dehydrate the Sea!

LOCK HIM UP!

...Who are hiding **UNDER THE SEA.**

Under

Experts believe these Fleas...

Unidentified Expert

...Could **ATTACK** at **ANY MOMENT!**

RAR!

And so, our world **TREMBLES** in **TERROR!**

Excellent!

The **Whole World** is **AFRAID!!!**

But we're the **Friendly Friends!**

We want to make everyone **HAPPY!**

We **ARE** GoinG to make everyone happy!!!

But **HOW?**

Well? What makes **YOU** GuYs happy?

LauGhinG!!! PLAYinG!!!

SmilinG!!! Cupcakes!!!

Those are **ALL** Good Answers...

...If YoU're **FiVe YEARS OLD!!!**

But some folks are more **COMPLEX!**

Some folks need **COMPLEX** things to make them happy.

Like what?

FEAR and **ANGER!!!**

Fear and Anger make people happy?

They sure Do!!!

BOOP

FEAR and ANGER trigger DopAmine Receptors in the BRAIN...

I ♡ DopAmine

...And **THAT** makes People **HAPPY!**

We've **ALREADY SCARED** them...

STOP THE SUBS

FLEAS GO HOME

Now we need to make them **MAD!**

But **HOW?**

OR, we could throw Pies at People!

Where did You Get those???

From the **Pie-MAKinG MAChine** in our kitchen!!!

Pies! Pies! Pies! Pies!

ALRight, if we're Going to throw **Pies** at People...

...we **HAVE** to do it **RiGHT!**

So there will be **No GiGGling**...

... **NO TOM-FOOLERY**...

... And **Most** **IMPORTANTLY**...

... **NO SinGing!**

And a **ONE**, and a **Two**, and a...

Nooooooooooo

Friendly Friends, Friendly Friends,
Flying Through A Cloud...

...We made up a
Second Verse...

...and we'll sing it
SUPA LOU-UD!

Friendly Friends,
Friendly Friends...

...Cozy, Cute,
and Clean...

Friendly Friends, Friendly Friends...

Um... hello.

What are you all doing?

nothin'.

Well, the whole World needs Your help...

...So **LET'S GO!!!**

No thanks.

Nobody wants to help **US**...

...why should we help **them?**

What's Going On Here???

Well, everybody hates my Papa.

Yeah, and they'll probably hate us, too...

...if **we** ever make a mistake.

So **we're** not taking **ANY** more chances!

Oh, I see.

So...

...if somebody gives you a hard time...

...You just **QUIT?**

Is that right?

Is **THAT** the way a **HERO** acts?

No. No.

OOH- People CAN be **MEAN**!!!

So Let's Just **Give UP**...

...because we're **ALL** a bunch of **Little bAbY**...

...**Quitters!!!**

We're sorry, Sarah.

You're darn right You're **SORRY!**

NOW Get up off of those butts...

...And Let's GO SAVE the WORLD!

And so...

FLIP FLOP FLIP FLOP FLIP

Sarah is the **SMARTEST PERSON EVER!**

I know!

HEY!!!

I SAID the SAME Thing a few Chapters ago!!!

Yeah...

...but it Sounded better when **She** said it.

CHAPTER 11

PIGGY MAKES HIS MOVE

Well, folks, we're back at the beach...

...where **FEAR** has turned to **OUTRAGE!!!**

SPLAT!

A **MASSIVE** Pie Fight has begun...

...and citizens are getting **HUFFIER AND PUFFIER!!!**

YOU'LL PAY FOR THAT!!!

But **I** didn't throw that Pie!

Well, it didn't Just fall out of the sky!

Good Point!

Authorities fear that everybody's **OUTRAGE**...

Anonymous Authority

...may cause them to Lose Focus...

What's-his-face

...on the **ReAL ISSue!**

Which is?

Umm...I forGot!

SPLOP!

FReeze, FLeAS!!!

Fleas?

Who are the FLeas?

Fleas?

Wait—Aren't You Guys **The FLEAS?**

No.

We're the **FriendLY Friends!**

Oh. Umm...

...Are we on the right Submarine?

Well, we **USED** to be "The Fleas"...

SIZE
-O-
TRON

SUPA DOOPA BIG
SUPA BIG
BIG
NORMAL
SMALL
SUPA SMALL
SUPA DOOPA SMALL
SUPA DOOPA POOPA SMALL
Okay, now you're just being silly.

SUPA DOO
SUPA BIG
BIG
NORMAL
SMALL
SUPA SMALL
SUPA DOOPA SMALL
SUPA DOOPA POOPA SMALL
Okay, now you're just being silly.

KA-
KLUNK

SUB WILL SHRINK
IN FIVE SECONDS...

SNAP

...FOUR...

... THREE ...

... TWO ...

166

All of my Problems...

...are getting smaller and smaller!!!

Bye-bye, **Losers!**

I think I'll send them all off...

...with a STANDING OVATION!

SLAP-O-RAMA

Let's get PIGGY with it!

Left hand here.

C'mon, Get SLAPPY!

Right Thumb here.

C'mon, Get SLAPPY!

CHAPTER 12

ZOOM IN

...is everybody okay?

Yeah, I think so.

WHAT happened?

It appears we've **SHRUNK** to **MICROSCOPIC SIZE!!!**

Status Report

You small!!!
....

Our sub was DAMAGED...

...we've lost our PROPELLER...

RRRRRRReeeeeeeeT

...AND WE'RE SLIDING INTO A SWEAT GLAND!!!

SSSSSLIP

Let's Just Grow BiG AGAin!!!

We CAN't!

OUR Size-o-Tron is BusTeD!!!

YAAAAAAAAAAAAAAA

Well, Goodbye, Bub!

So Long, Crunky!

We need someone to dive into the **ABYSS**...

... and fetch our **PROPELLER!**

Somebody who's not afraid to Get **STINKY!!!**

Do we have any voluntee—

SWISH!!

HEY, DOG MAN! WAIT UP!!!

PLOP

PLIP

PLEEP

Now it's time to **Fix** this **Sub!**

AYE, AYE, CAPTAIN!

The three brave friends swam **Down...**

... and brought the Propeller back **UP!**

But then...

CHAPTER 13

THIS MITE BE A PROBLEM

The propeller was recovered...

...and reattached...

This is Glue. STRONG Stuff!

...and soon the damaged sub...

This is tape. Strong stuff!

...was set to soar again!!!

This is acrylic Latex caulk. Strong stuff!

I think we're ready to go!!!

What could possibly go wrong???

But then...

RAAAR!!!

Help! It's A Giant Monster!

Actually, it's really Just a **Microscopic** Parasitic Mite...

...of the Genus: **Demodex**.

In small numbers, they're quite harmless!

UNCLE LARRY!

This looks like a Job for the **SUPA BUDDIES!**

We need our costumes!!!

And so...

WE ARE HURRY UPPING!

You Guys can't be the **SUPA Buddies**...

... if You don't Got **80-HD!!!**

She's right! 80-HD's hands are **FULL!**

Maybe I can take his place.

But You don't have a costume!

We're doing SomeThing IMPORTANT! Gee Whiz!!!

And So...

I look **Awesome!**

Thanks, 80-HD!

Now we Just need to think up my SUPERHERO NAME!

You're too late, Kid! GRRR! Be nice, Zuzu!!!

I think everybody Got **SWALLOWED!**

HEY!!!

YOU LET GO OF OUR FRIENDS!

Mitey Fighty

Right
Thumb
here.

Mitey Fighty

CHAPTER 14

AND Then THERE WERE TWO

Wait a minute.

It's not **Just** Fear...

...it's **ANGER**, too!

Oh, Yeah!!!

But how do we—

Pies!!!

...You Give us back OUR Friends!!!

RAAAR!

Don't YOU TALK BACK to ME!

WHO Do You THiNk You ARE?

THiS is MY HOUSE!!!

Hey, Uncle Larry? Yes?

Can we Grow **SUPA DOOPA BiG**?

Gosh! We've never Tried **ThAT** before!

Size -o- TRON

Let's do it!!!

KA KLUNK

Size -o- TRON

SUB WILL GROW IN FIVE SECONDS...

... FOUR ...

CHAPTER 15

EXACTLY ONE HUNDRED AND NINE SECONDS EARLIER

Well, **That** was easy!!!

I robbed **Five** banks today...

... and nobody even **Noticed!**

They're All too busy being **SCARED** and **ANGRY!!!**

Beach

Nobody is Paying Attention to the **REAL Problem**...

... which is **ME!!!**

Now it's time to **RELAX** in my **LUXURIOUS NEW CASTLE...**

PIGWARTS

...which I just purchased with my **ILL-GOTTEN GAINS!!!**

PIGWARTS

Aah—This is the **Life!**

Root Beer

What could **POSSIBLY** go wrong?

But then...

WAAAAAAAAA

CLOP!

Wow!!! Look how Little PiGGY is !!!

Aww— He's **SO CUTE!!!**

Can we keep him?

Chapter 16

In Search of the Depth

KA-KLUNK

SIZE
-O-
TRON

SUPA DOOPA BiG
SUPA BiG
BiG
NORMAL
SMALL
SUPA SMALL

SHA SHA SHA

And in the end,
old friends...

...new friends...

...and friends we sort of forGot about ten chapters ago...

...all worked toGether...

...to help Petey rebuild his lab.

227

Soon, it was time to stop for the day.

Let's all Go to DoG Man's house!

We can eat Supper together!

HOORAY!!!

And So...

Thanks for all of your **Kindness**, everyone.

I Told you we'd find somebody to help you, Wally!

But...

...but why <u>Me</u>?

That's why we're here, Papa...

...to help each other.

It's like the sea, Petey...

You can just dip your toes in...

...or you can **FATHOM** the SoundLess Depths.

That's what **I** was talking about...

...back in Chapter **5**!!!

You can do the **BARE Minimum**...

...and **SLIDE** through life...

...or You can **Give MORE**...

...Give what **YOU** didn't Get...

...LOVE MORE...

...And DROP the OLD STORY!!!

THAT was my WHOLE POINT!!!

Yeah, we know...

...but it **ALWAYS** sounds better when **SHE** says it!!!

HOW 2 DRAW Mike the FLY

in 22 Ridiculously easy steps!

236

WHO **STILL** hasn't figured out her **super hero** name Yet!!!

in **16** Ridiculously easy steps!

① ② ③ ④ ⑤ ⑥ ⑦ ⑧

⑨ ⑩ ⑪ ⑫ ⑬

⑭ ⑮ ⑯

FOR MORE "HOW 2 DRAW" Fun...

...ViSiT PLANETPILKEY.COM

★ "Irreverent, laugh-out-Loud funny, and . . . downright moving."
— Publishers Weekly, starred review

TH DAV PILKEY!

The epic musical adventure is now available from Broadway Records!

Go to PlanetPilkey.com to join Dav Pilkey's Epic Comic Club, read chapters, watch videos, and make comics!

NOTES & FUN FACTS

✮ The most common English-language translation of the title of Jules Verne's *Vingt Mille Lieues Sous Les Mers* is <u>20,000 Leagues Under the Sea</u>. This is a mistranslation, however. It should be "Seas."

✮ The mistranslation implies a depth of 20,000 leagues, which is impossible because 20,000 Leagues is over TWICE the circumference of the Earth.

✮ Studies have shown that false or misleading news (chapters 7 and 8) often spreads faster than legitimate news.
BuzzFeedNews, November 16, 2016.

✮ Scientists have found that fear and anger (Chapter 9) are linked to dopamine, a neurotransmitter that causes people to feel pleasure.
Psychology Today, August 25, 2015; Scientific American, July 14, 2008.

✮ Demodex mites (Chapter 13) are real, microscopic creatures. Here are some facts about them:
* They live on the skin of mammals (including humans and pigs).
* They have eight legs.
* Their favorite food is pumpkin pie.
* They typically come out at night.
* They are probably on your face right now.

✮ One of the "facts" about Demodex mites mentioned above is not true. Can you guess which one?

✮ The design for Uncle Larry's flying submarine was loosely inspired by illustrations produced for a Japanese publication. They were created by an artist who signed each painting: "Kyo-62."

✮ Chapter 16's title is based on the quote, "Hast thou walked in the search of the depth?" from Job 38:16 (KJV). It appears in the final paragraph of some English-language versions of <u>20,000 Leagues Under the Seas.</u>

✮ Other English-language versions substitute "Who can fathom the soundless depths?" (based on Ecclesiastes 7:24), which Sarah refers to on page 230.

✮ "Give More. Give what you didn't get. Love more. Drop the old story." is a quote from the journals of Garry Shandling.

✮ Molly and Li'l Petey continued working on their comic WALLY'S WORLD and finally finished it. You can read the ENTIRE comic for free at Dav Pilkey's Epic Comic Club (PlanetPilkey.com) starting on June 1, 2023.